Editor
Polly Hoffman

Managing Editor
Ina Massler Levin, M.A.

Editor-in-Chief
Sharon Coan, M.S. Ed.

Illustrators
Wendy Chang
Blanca Apodaca

Cover Artist
Barb Lorseyedi

Art Coordinator
Denice Adorno

Imaging
James Edward Grace
Rosa C. See

Product Manager
Phil Garcia

Publishers
Rachelle Cracchiolo, M.S. Ed.
Mary Dupuy Smith, M.S. Ed.

Collaborative Activities
for a Year-Long Memory Book

Use for:
- Back to School Night
- Open House
- Parent Conferences
- Year-End Take-Home Portfolio

Authors

Sherry Pate, M.A.; Michelle Hancock; and Jennie VanHaelst

Teacher Created Materials, Inc.
6421 Industry Way
Westminster, CA 92683
www.teachercreated.com

ISBN-0-7439-3088-6

©2001 Teacher Created Materials, Inc.
Made in U.S.A.

Table of Contents

Introduction

Math

Shapes

Number Activities

Print Numbers

Patterns/Graphing

Addition/Subtraction

Fractions

Telling Time

Money

Language Arts

Sentence Stems and Student Stories

Table of Contents (cont.)

Introduction

A Quick Look

This book serves a tri-fold purpose in the K/1 classroom. First, it is a keepsake that students will cherish for many years containing special memories of the school year, the celebration of special events, holidays and other activities in which they have participated, a record of their fellow classmates who have become good friends, and a collection of the hard work they have done throughout the year. This will give each student a feeling of pride and accomplishment.

Second, the yearbook provides the teacher with a complete progress portfolio of the childrens' work throughout the school year, making the job of assessing skills and keeping a record of the skills mastered a much easier task. The portfolio form of assessment has been adopted in many school districts. This book enables the teacher to, at a glance, review the progress of the student. Because student work and assessment are both included in one book, the process of assessment is greatly simplified. The teacher, having a record of student progress thus far, can also plan instruction more easily to provide remediation as well as enrichment.

Third, this yearbook is an excellent tool for the teacher to use in parent/teacher conferences. Parents benefit greatly from seeing a record of their child's growth academically and socially over the school year. They also thoroughly enjoy the personalized approach of the yearbook, which includes a keepsake record of the special events and new friends their child has made throughout the year.

How to Use This Book

This book can be customized for the specific skills and themes upon which the teacher chooses to focus on at either the kindergarten or first grade level. The teacher can simply select and duplicate the pages that he/she wishes to use. For example, a school may not celebrate various holidays and the teacher would not duplicate those pages for use with her/his students. Teachers may choose not to duplicate pages in which skills are considered too advanced for their particular class.

On your supply list for the upcoming school year, include a pocketed folder with center brads (one per child) specifically for the purpose of this yearbook. Prior to the beginning of school, select the appropriate cover page (either kindergarten or first grade) and duplicate one per student. Also select the math and language arts pages to use for the entire school year and have them copied. Pages selected should be based on district goals, themes, special events, and activities on which you plan to focus. There are some pages (such as number and letter identification and letter/sound correspondence) that may be duplicated more than once to place in the yearbook and used throughout the school year indicating progress made in mastering these skills. All the pages are placed in the students' folders that they personalize by decorating the cover and making it their own. It is easiest to keep these folders together in a central location in the classroom. Then just "pull them" prior to instruction or assessment. As lesson plans are finalized each week, look through the yearbook to determine the specific pages to highlight. Direct instruction or student completion of pages as follow-up, or math or language arts assessment are possibilities. Also, glancing through each student's yearbook on a bi-weekly basis helps the teacher stay updated on student progress in mastering the skills.

Introduction *(cont.)*

How to Use This Book *(cont.)*

The yearbook is also useful in the classroom for informal, as well as formal, conferencing with staff members and parents. It is ideal to have the yearbooks available at Open House, for the children to share with their parents. Duplicate specific completed pages of each student's yearbook to place in his or her academic progress file to keep a record that will remain at school. Depending on the individual needs of students and teaching situations, different pages may need to be duplicated some years. Duplicating the same pages for each student in the classroom will make it easier to conduct small and large group instruction, or individual assessment. However, each student's book may be individualized by duplicating only those pages that that student is to complete. This type of modification may be necessary at times, as all students will not be at the same developmental level. Teachers should also add pages to personalize the yearbook.

Pages have been included for use from the beginning to the end of the school year. Students will be anxious to bring their yearbooks home at the end of the year, complete with samples of their work, a record of the special events that took place, and new friends made during the year.

Sample Lesson Plan

Teachers may choose to use the student pages in one of two ways: as a general follow-up activity to direct instruction, or as a formal, one-on-one assessment of skill mastery in conjunction with district or state outcomes or standards.

When using one of the pages in conjunction with classroom instruction as a follow-up activity, utilize the following format:

1. The teacher specifies the objective on which to focus and selects a page that corresponds to that objective. For example:

    Objective: The student will put in order a series of three pictures, demonstrating the skill of sequencing.

2. The teacher organizes a lesson plan, including the use of the student page, as a follow-up to instruction, deciding if he or she can best accomplish the objective using individual, small group, or large group instruction (or a combination of the above). For example: During shared reading time, the teacher reads a big book with the class, followed by a discussion of the story events. On a large sheet of paper, list the events of the story in order, perhaps even illustrating the events. Then discuss the concepts of first, next, and last based on the events listed. It may be helpful to discuss elements of the school day, drawing pictures together of the first, second, and last events of the school day.

Then, as a small group activity for kindergarten (or a whole group activity for first grade), each student is given his/her yearbook and directed to find the page assigned. (Place a self-stick page marker in each student's book at the appropriate page prior to instruction to make finding the page easier).

Introduction *(cont.)*

Sample Lesson Plan *(cont.)*

After each student finds the page, discuss the pictures found on the page and again discuss the concept that some things happen first, next, and last. Each student is directed to look again at the pictures and decide if the picture should have a number 1, 2, or 3 (corresponding to first, next, and last events). The class can do this together either as a small or large group with the teacher and students talking through each example and writing 1, 2, and 3 for picture events, or, students can each complete their sheet individually with the teacher circulating among the students to ascertain if the students are completing the page correctly.

As this is a progress portfolio, the teacher may choose to indicate at the top of the page if the page was completed as a group or individually (or if the student needed help in correctly completing the page).

After each student completes the page, the group may discuss their answers and the teacher may provide additional reinforcement by doing more sequencing activities at this time or at a different time in the school day.

To use the numerous pages of sentence stems in the language arts section, teachers should lead a group discussion of the topic or holiday. Following related activities, students may either dictate their response for the teacher to record; or use approximated spelling or conventional spelling in recording their responses on their own.

When using any of the pages as individual assessment pages for skill mastery, the following format is recommended:

1. After the objective has been selected and instruction has been presented, the teacher assesses skill mastery by choosing the corresponding page in the yearbook for use with the individual student.

   For example, during the school year, the teacher wishes to assess the level of mastery of identification of letters based on the instruction that has been given over a period of time (such as a semester).

2. The teacher works with one student at a time while the others, for example, are reading books or doing another independent activity so the teacher and one student can work undisturbed for 5-10 minutes.

3. Turning to the page in the yearbook that addresses identification of uppercase and lowercase letters, the teacher points to each letter, asking the child to identify the letter. For each correct response, the teacher places a checkmark next to the corresponding letter.

4. The teacher then works with each student individually for 5 to 10 minutes (over a period of several days or a week) completing the identical assessment.

5. The teacher may wish to record the results of the assessment on a classroom list in which each child's score is available at a glance and/or in a child's individual file for quick reference. (Teachers may also want to duplicate the student page to place in a child's progress file and/or send home with the child to keep parents updated on their child's progress).

Math Outcomes

Below are the math outcomes that are addressed in this book. You may wish to duplicate these as a checklist to use with students and parents throughout the school year. Place a checkmark on the line in front of the skill to show that the student has mastered the skill.

The student will be able to:

Shapes

_____ Describe and name shapes

_____ Draw shapes

_____ Compare shapes that are the same and different

_____ Make patterns out of shapes

Numbers

_____ Count 1–10

_____ Count 1–20

_____ Count 1–50

_____ Count 1–100

_____ Identify numbers 1–10

_____ Identify numbers 1–20

_____ Identify numbers 1–50

_____ Identify numbers 1–100

_____ Count objects to match a given number

_____ Match a number to the same number of objects

_____ Count by 2's, 5's, and 10's

_____ Match numbers to number words

_____ Fill out a monthly calendar

Patterns

_____ Continue a pattern

_____ Make a pattern

_____ Recognize patterns

_____ Use patterns to order and count objects

Graphs

_____ Read graphs and organize data on graphs

_____ Collect data and record it

_____ Compare data on graphs

Addition/Subtraction

_____ Form addition and subtraction number sentences

_____ Make different combinations to form specific sums

_____ Change groups by adding or removing group members

_____ Solve simple addition problems

_____ Solve simple subtraction problems

_____ Estimation/Probability

_____ Estimate which group has the most/least

_____ Predict a reasonable number of objects

Fractions

_____ Recognize a whole

_____ Recognize a half

Time

_____ Tell time on the hour

_____ Tell time on the half-hour

Money

_____ Recognize coins

_____ State the value of coins

_____ Count combinations of coins to one dollar

Language Arts Outcomes

Below are the language arts outcomes addressed in this book. You may wish to reproduce these and use it as a checklist to utilize with students and parents throughout the school year. Place a checkmark on the line in front of skills that the student has mastered.

The student will be able to:

Reading/Book Use

_____ Indicate that print conveys meaning

_____ Identify letters

_____ Identify sounds

_____ Identify beginning sounds

_____ Identify medial sounds

_____ Identify ending sounds

_____ Match letters and words that are the same

_____ Use environmental print

_____ Identify rhyme

_____ Identify sight words

_____ Complete a sentence stem

Writing

_____ Copy letters

_____ Write first name

_____ Write last name

_____ Copy words and phrases

_____ Use developmental spelling

_____ Write random letters

_____ Write correct first letter

_____ Write correct last letter

_____ Write most consonant sounds

_____ Write some whole words

_____ Use word spacing

_____ Use capital letters

_____ Demonstrate a writing vocabulary

_____ Write friendly letter

_____ Address envelope

Language/Concepts

_____ Identify colors

_____ Identify first name

_____ Identify last name

_____ Identify first, next, and last

_____ Identify positions (up, down, in, out, etc.)

_____ Identify opposites

_____ Demonstrate understanding of real and make believe

_____ Sequence events presented in pictures

_____ Sequence events in a story

_____ Demonstrate understanding of cause/effect

_____ Identify rhyme

_____ Classify objects

_____ State the days of the week

_____ State the months of the year

_____ Sequence days of the week

Fine Motor

_____ Color

_____ Cut

_____ Print first name

_____ Print last name

_____ Print letters

Reproduce this page to use as the yearbook cover.

My Kindergarten Yearbook

by

_____

Reproduce this page to use as the yearbook cover.

My
First
Grade
Yearbook

by

_____

_____

Shapes

Directions: Identify the shapes at the top of the page. Draw the shapes in the space at the bottom of the page.

I can identify the shapes.

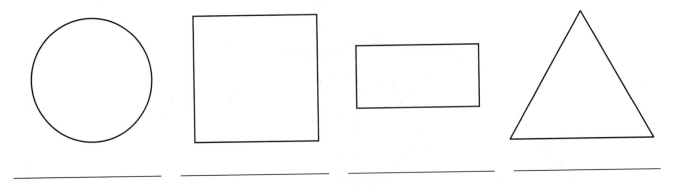

I can draw the shapes.

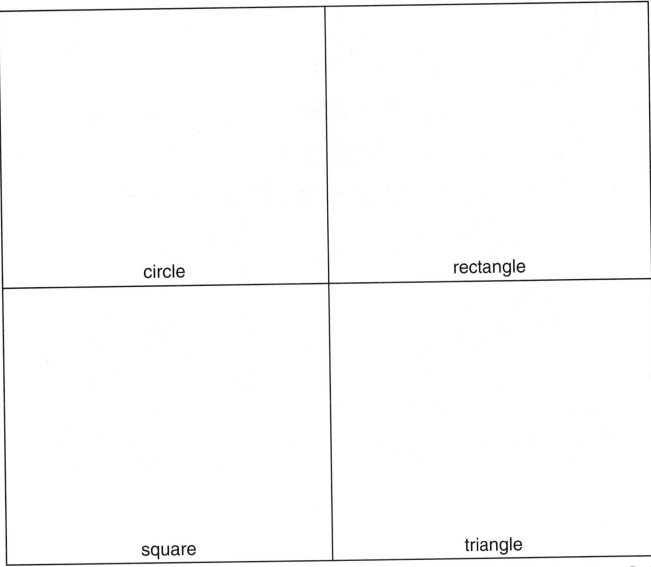

Shape Counting

Directions: Draw an "**X**" on the group of shapes that has the most.

Directions: Draw one more of the same shape at the end of each row.

Same Shapes

Color Key

Color the shapes   ◯ red   ▭ blue

                                 ◻ green   △ yellow

Color the first shape in each row. Then color the shapes that are the same as the first one in each row. Use the Color Key.

Shapes of Christmas

Directions: Draw a picture of a Christmas tree using triangles △ and rectangles ☐ for the tree, and circles ○ for the ornaments.

How many triangles △, rectangles ☐, and circles ○ did you use?

I used _____ triangles.   △

I used _____ rectangles.   ☐

I used _____ circles.   ○

Shape Faces

Directions: Follow the directions and use the correct color for each shape face.

Color the ◯ green. Color the ◇ red.

Color the ▢ blue. Color the △ yellow.

Color the ▯ orange.

Shape Patterns

Directions: Follow the directions for each section below.

Circle "Yes" if it is a pattern, circle "No" if it is not.

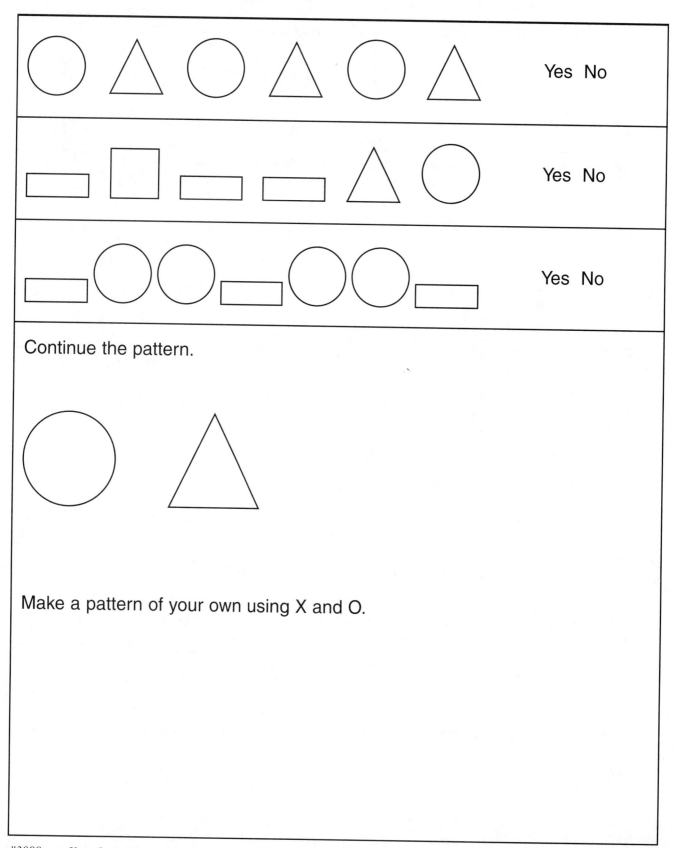

Yes No

Yes No

Yes No

Continue the pattern.

Make a pattern of your own using X and O.

Shape Graph

Teacher Directions: Give each student a small bag containing triangles and squares. Have the student color in the correct number of spaces for the triangles and squares. At the bottom, have the student record the number of squares and triangles. Take time to talk with the students about which shape has more or less.

	△	□
8		
7		
6		
5		
4		
3		
2		
1		

I have _____ triangles.

I have _____ squares.

Number Match

Directions: Draw a line to match the number on the left to the number on the right.

Left	Right
8	9
1	4
2	7
5	5
3	8
9	6
4	2
7	1
6	3

I Can Count

Counting by Ones

Teacher Directions: Have students rote count aloud by ones. Record how far they can count on the line below. We recommend doing this three times during the year (beginning, middle and end).

I can count to _____ .	Date _____
I can count to _____ .	Date _____
I can count to _____ .	Date _____

Skip Counting

Teacher Directions: Have students skip count aloud by 2's, 5's, and 10's to 100. Mark down the date they mastered the skill on the line provided.

I can skip count by 10s to 100.	Date _____
I can skip count by 5s to 100.	Date _____
I can skip count by 2s to 100.	Date _____

Notes:

Count the Bees

Directions: Count the number of bees in each hive. Write the number on the line next to the hive.

Count the Acorns

Directions: Count the number of acorns in each box. Circle the correct number.

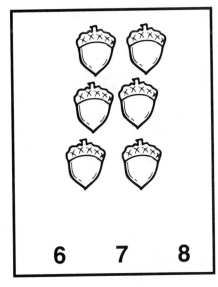

6 7 8

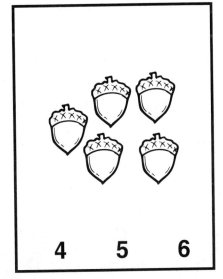

10 11 12

4 5 6

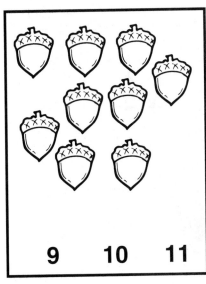

9 10 11

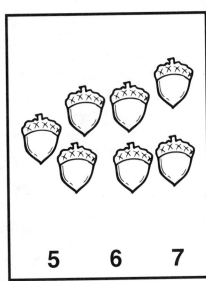

5 6 7

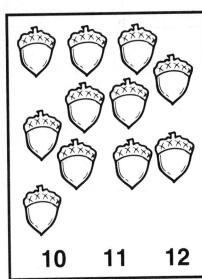

10 11 12

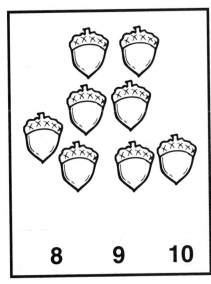

8 9 10

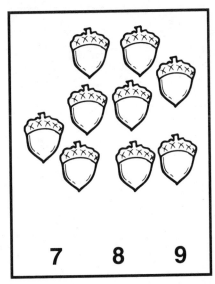

7 8 9

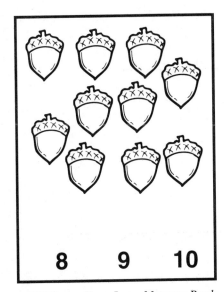

8 9 10

Halloween Counting

Directions: Look at the picture. Write the correct number for each symbol on the line next to it.

How many ? _____

How many ? _____

How many ? _____

How many ? _____

How many ? _____

How many ? _____

Hanukkah Candle Counting

Teacher Directions: Read a story about the Jewish holiday of Hanukkah. Discuss the lighting of the menorah and why there are nine candles. Also, talk about the significance and order of when to light each candle. Then, have each student color the menorah below and write the numbers on the candles in the order in which they are lit.

Today we read a story about the Jewish holiday of Hanukkah. One thing I learned about the Holiday of Hanukkah was

_____

_____

_____

Snowflake Counting

Directions: Count the number of snowflakes in each rectangle. Write the correct number of snowflakes in the box provided.

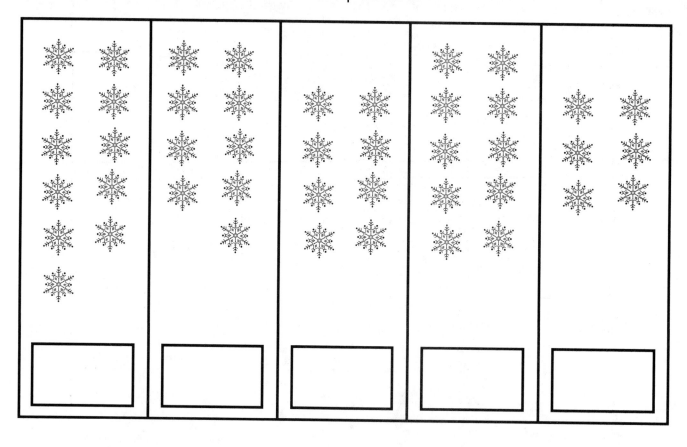

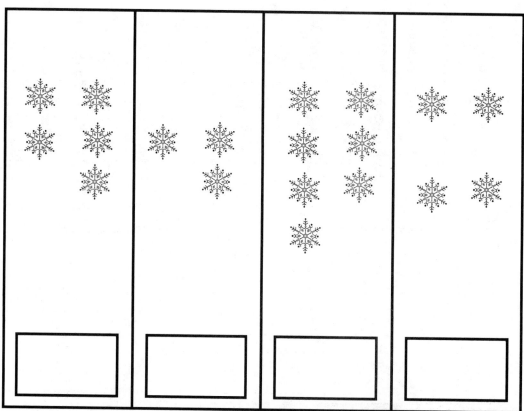

Number and Object Match

Directions: Draw a line to match the number on the left to the box with the matching number of cubes on the right.

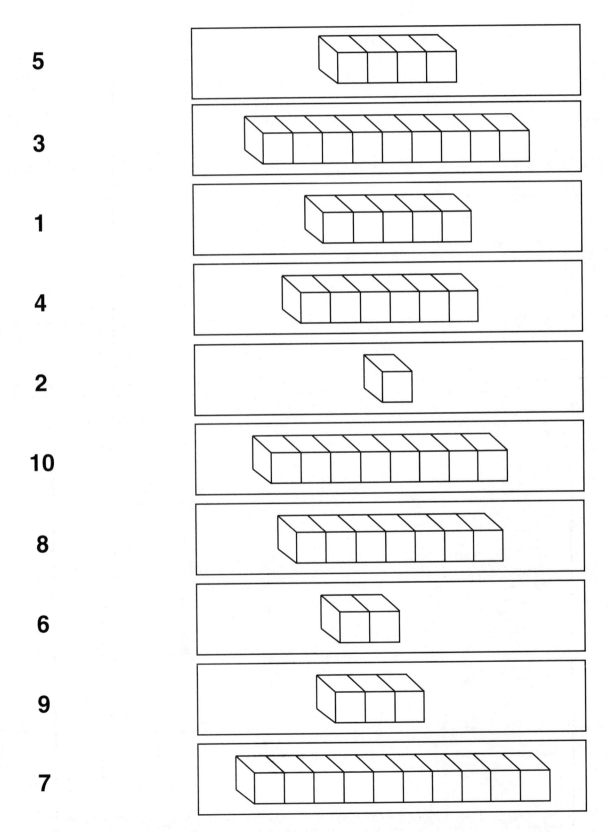

Count and Stamp

Teacher Directions: Have students look at the number on the left. Have them use a "tiny" stamp and inkpad to stamp the correct number of objects represented on the left. If a stamp and inkpad are not available, use a marker and draw the correct number of shapes, letters, etc.

5	
3	
1	
2	
4	
10	
6	
8	
7	
9	

Identification of Numbers 1-10

Teacher Directions: Show the student the numbers below and have the student tell you what each number is. You may also use flashcards instead of these numbers. It is recommended doing this three times during the school year (beginning, middle and end). Record the date and correct numbers on the lines below.

3   5   1   6   2

4   8   7   10   9

Date: _____ I know these numbers: _____

3   5   1   6   2

4   8   7   10   9

Date: _____ I know these numbers: _____

3   5   1   6   2

4   8   7   10   9

Date: _____ I know these numbers: _____

Identification of Numbers 1-20

Teacher Directions: Show the student the numbers below and have the student tell you what each number is. You may also use flashcards instead of the numbers below. It is recommended doing this three times during the school year (beginning, middle, and end). Record the date and numbers correct on the lines below.

12	3	16	1	6	2	11
14	4	8	5	10	9	15
13	19	18	7	20	17	

Date: _____ I know these numbers: _____

12	3	16	1	6	2	11
14	4	8	5	10	9	15
13	19	18	7	20	17	

Date: _____ I know these numbers: _____

12	3	16	1	6	2	11
14	4	8	5	10	9	15
13	19	18	7	20	17	

Date: _____ I know these numbers: _____

I Know My Number Words!

Directions: Draw a line to match the number word to the correct number.

three	6
ten	2
six	7
four	1
one	5
five	10
seven	4
two	8
eight	3
nine	9

I Can Print My Numbers!

Directions: In the space next to each number, trace the shaded number and then print the number on the empty lines.

1   1 _____ _____ _____ _____

2   2 _____ _____ _____ _____

3   3 _____ _____ _____ _____

4   4 _____ _____ _____ _____

5   5 _____ _____ _____ _____

6   6 _____ _____ _____ _____

7   7 _____ _____ _____ _____

8   8 _____ _____ _____ _____

9   9 _____ _____ _____ _____

10   10 _____ _____ _____ _____

Missing Numbers 1-10

Directions: Trace the numbers, and when you come to a blank space, write in the missing number.

1 2 3 ___ 5 6 7 8 ___ 10

1 2 ___ 4 5 6 ___ 8 9 10

1 2 3 4 ___ 6 7 ___ 9 10

1 ___ 3 4 5 6 7 8 9 ___

___ 2 3 4 5 ___ 7 8 9 10

Skip Counting Fill In

Teacher Directions: Have students fill in the missing numbers with a red pencil, marker, or crayon. Explain to the students that the numbers in red are the numbers used when counting by 5's. Explain to the students that the end numbers represent counting by 10's.

1	2	3	4		6	7	8	9	
11	12	13	14		16	17	18	19	
21	22	23	24		26	27	28	29	
31	32	33	34		36	37	38	39	
41	42	43	44		46	47	48	49	
51	52	53	54		56	57	58	59	
61	62	63	64		66	67	68	69	
71	72	73	74		76	77	78	79	
81	82	83	84		86	87	88	89	
91	92	93	94		96	97	98	99	

Fill in the Missing Numbers 1–100

Directions: Trace the numbers on the chart. When you come to a blank space, fill in the missing number.

1	2	3	4	5	6	7	8	9	
	12		14	15			18		
21		23		25		27			30
		33	34		36		38	39	
41		43		45		47	48		50
	52		54		56	57		59	
61		63		65	66		68		70
	72		74			77		79	
81		83		85			88		90
	92		94		96	97			100

Number Grid 1-100

Teacher Directions: Give students the grid below. Have them practice tracing the numbers 1-100. When they can trace the numbers, give them the blank number grid and have them fill in the numbers 1-100. They may use the number grid as a guide. This grid, along with the blank grid, can provide good practice at a math center.

1	2	3	4	5	6	7	8	9	10
11	12	13	14	15	16	17	18	19	20
21	22	23	24	25	26	27	28	29	30
31	32	33	34	35	36	37	38	39	40
41	42	43	44	45	46	47	48	49	50
51	52	53	54	55	56	57	58	59	60
61	62	63	64	65	66	67	68	69	70
71	72	73	74	75	76	77	78	79	80
81	82	83	84	85	86	87	88	89	90
91	92	93	94	95	96	97	98	99	100

Blank Grid 1-100

Teacher Directions: Use this blank grid, along with the number grid from the previous page, and have students fill in the numbers 1-100. When the students can do this, see how far they can fill in the grid without a guide. The grids can be reproduced and used for math centers.

Number Grid 101-200

Teacher Directions: Give this grid to the students. Have them practice tracing the numbers 101-200. When they can trace the numbers, give them the blank number grid and have them fill in the numbers 101-200. They may use the number grid as a guide. This grid, along with the blank grid, can provide good practice at a math center.

101	102	103	104	105	106	107	108	109	110
111	112	113	114	115	116	117	118	119	120
121	122	123	124	125	126	127	128	129	130
131	132	133	134	135	136	137	138	139	140
141	142	143	144	145	146	147	148	149	150
151	152	153	154	155	156	157	158	159	160
161	162	163	164	165	166	167	168	169	170
171	172	173	174	175	176	177	178	179	180
181	182	183	184	185	186	187	188	189	190
191	192	193	194	195	196	197	198	199	200

Blank Grid 101-200

Teacher Directions: Use this blank grid, along with the number grid from the previous page, and have students fill in the numbers 101-200. When the students can do this, see how far they can fill in the grid without a guide. The grids can be reproduced and used for math centers.

Calendar Page

Teacher Directions: Fill in the calendar with the correct numbers. In the space at the top, write in the month and draw a picture to go with your calendar. Encourage your students to draw a picture that corresponds with the season. Teachers may provide a model for the students or indicate the starting date for the calendar. This blank calendar can be good practice at a math center each month.

Sunday	Monday	Tuesday	Wednesday	Thursday	Friday	Saturday

Bear Patterns

Directions: Use crayons to color the bears so that they make a pattern. You may want to practice with plastic bears or blocks first.

I can make a pattern with different color bears.

Directions: Look at the graph below. Count how many big bears there are and print the number on the line next to the big bear. Count how many small bears there are and print the number on the line next to the small bears.

My Bear Graph

big	🧸	🧸	🧸							
small	🧸	🧸	🧸	🧸						
	1	2	3	4	5	6	7	8	9	10

There are _____ big bears.

There are _____ small bears.

Note: Teachers are encouraged to discuss which line has more bears and which has less.

How Do We Get to School?

Teacher Directions: Make a copy of this paper or write the information on the chalkboard for each student. As a group fill in the missing information. Help the younger students fill in the graph with the class information. Older students may be able to fill in the graph by themselves. Conclude the activity with a class discussion about the information shown on the graph.

How Our Class Gets to School

	1	2	3	4	5	6	7	8	9	10	11	12	13	14	15
ride the bus															
walk															
are driven to school															
ride a bike															
other (skateboard, scooter)															

In our class:

_____ children ride the bus to school.

_____ children ride their bikes to school.

_____ children are driven to school.

_____ children walk to school.

_____ other

Candy-Coated Chocolates Pattern and Graph

Teacher Directions: Give each student a bag containing *yellow*, *green*, and *brown* candy-coated chocolates. Ask them to use the candies to create a pattern on the circles at the top of the page. Then, use crayons to color the circles the same colors as the candies. Discuss with students the information that was gained by making the graph. These materials may also be reproduced and used at a math center.

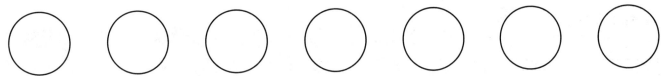

Directions: Use the candy to fill in the graph below. Color each section of the graph to represent one of the colors of candies in the bag. At the bottom of the graph, fill in the sentences with the correct number for each color of candy coated chocolates.

yellow										
green										
brown										
	1	2	3	4	5	6	7	8	9	10

 I have _____ yellow candies.

I have _____ green candies.

I have _____ brown candies.

Christmas Tree Graph

Teacher Directions: Make a copy of this paper or write the information on the chalkboard for the students. As a group, fill in the missing information. Younger students may need help filling in the graph. Older students may be able to fill in the graph by themselves. A good way to end this activity is with a class discussion about the information shown on the graph.

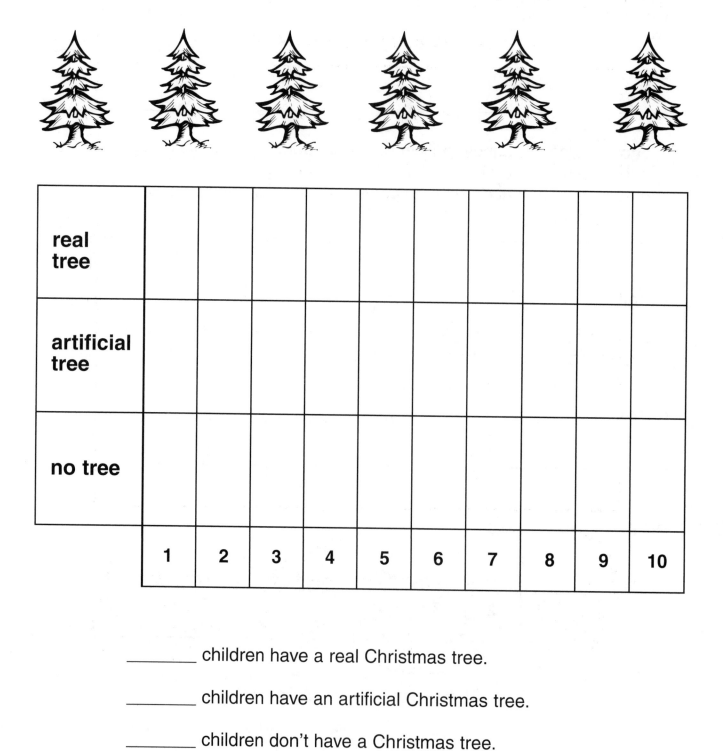

real tree										
artificial tree										
no tree										
	1	2	3	4	5	6	7	8	9	10

_____ children have a real Christmas tree.

_____ children have an artificial Christmas tree.

_____ children don't have a Christmas tree.

Collecting Data

Directions: Take this graph around to five friends and ask them what they like best: ice cream, cake, candy, or fruit. Write their name in the correct box on the graph. For example, if they like cake best, then sign their name in a box in the cake column. Fill in the sentence at the bottom of the page with the name of the food that your friends liked the best.

What do your friends like best?

Ice cream   Cake   Candy   Fruit

My friends like _____ the best.

Candy Heart Pattern and Graph

Teacher Directions: Give each student a bag containing pink, yellow, orange, and purple conversation candy hearts. Have the students create a graph based on how many hearts they have of each color. Discuss with the students the information that was gained by making the graph. These materials may also be reproduced and used as a math center.

Directions: Use the candy hearts to fill in the graph below. Color each section of the graph to represent one of the groups of hearts in the bag. If you have four purple hearts, color four spaces in the purple column. At the bottom of the graph, fill in the blanks according to how many hearts you have of each color.

Conversation Heart Graph

pink										
yellow										
orange										
purple										
	1	2	3	4	5	6	7	8	9	10

I have _____ pink candy hearts.

I have _____ yellow candy hearts.

I have _____ orange candy hearts.

I have _____ purple candy hearts.

Shamrock Graph

Teacher Directions: Give each student a bag containing green, black, and yellow shamrocks. Have them fill in the graph using the shamrocks in their bag. They may color one section of the graph to represent each of the shamrocks in their bag. At the bottom of the graph, fill in the correct number for each color of shamrock. Discuss with the students what information was gained by making the graph. The materials will also make a good resource for math centers.

	1	2	3	4	5	6	7
green							
yellow							
black							

I have _____ green shamrocks.

I have _____ yellow shamrocks.

I have _____ black shamrocks.

Jellybean Patterns

Directions: Look at the jellybeans below. If the row shows a pattern circle yes, if not circle no.

Yes   No

Yes   No

Yes   No

Directions: Create your own the jellybean patterns below.

Teacher Directions: Give each student a small bag of jellybeans and ask them to make patterns with them on the lines below. Have them trace and color the patterns to look like jellybeans.

Name Graph

Teacher Directions: Reproduce this page or copy the information on the chalkboard for the students. As a group, fill in the missing information. Help younger students fill in the graph with the class information. Older students may be able to fill in the graph by themselves. At the conclusion of the activity, lead a class discussion about the information shown on the graph.

How many letters are in your first name?

	1	2	3	4	5	6	7	8	9	10	11	12	13	14
Other														
8 letters														
7 letters														
6 letters														
5 letters														
4 letters														
3 letters														

Coin Graph

Teacher Directions: Give each student a bag containing pennies, nickels, and dimes. Have them fill in the graph using the coins in their bag. They may use coin stamps or color the sections of the graph to represent each of the coins in their bag. They should then answer the questions below the graph. Discuss with students what information was gained by making the graph. The materials may also be reproduced and used for a math center.

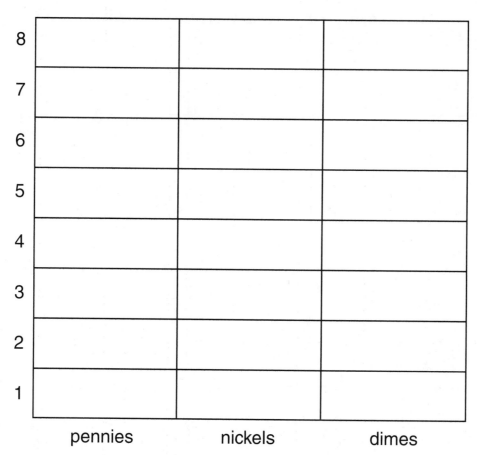

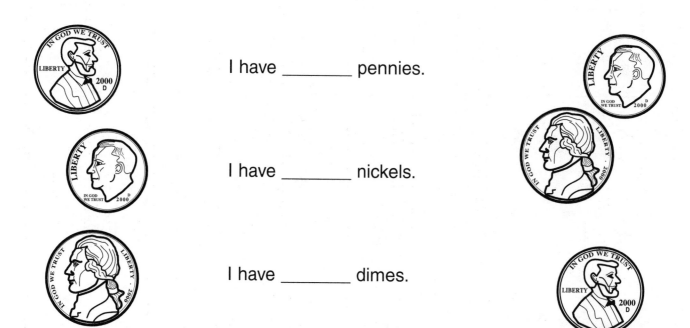

I have _____ pennies.

I have _____ nickels.

I have _____ dimes.

Sink or Float Data

Teacher Directions: Fill a water table or dishpan with tap water. Lay out a paper clip, marble, cork, pencil, and straw. Have each child place the items, one at a time, in the water. On the graph below they should record the information learned. If the item floats, mark the float column. If it sinks, mark the sink column. Discuss with students the information learned.

	Sink	Float
paper clip		
marble		
cork		
pencil		
straw		

Freddie Gets Five

Directions: Give Freddie five balls in each box. If there aren't enough balls in the box, draw more balls in the box. If there are too many balls in the box, cross off the extra balls using an "X."

Dinosaur Combinations of Seven

Directions: Count the number of dinosaurs in each row. Write the number under each row on the line provided. Count both rows of dinosaurs to make sure they equal seven. You may also use manipulatives to represent each dinosaur in the row and then count them to see that together they equal seven.

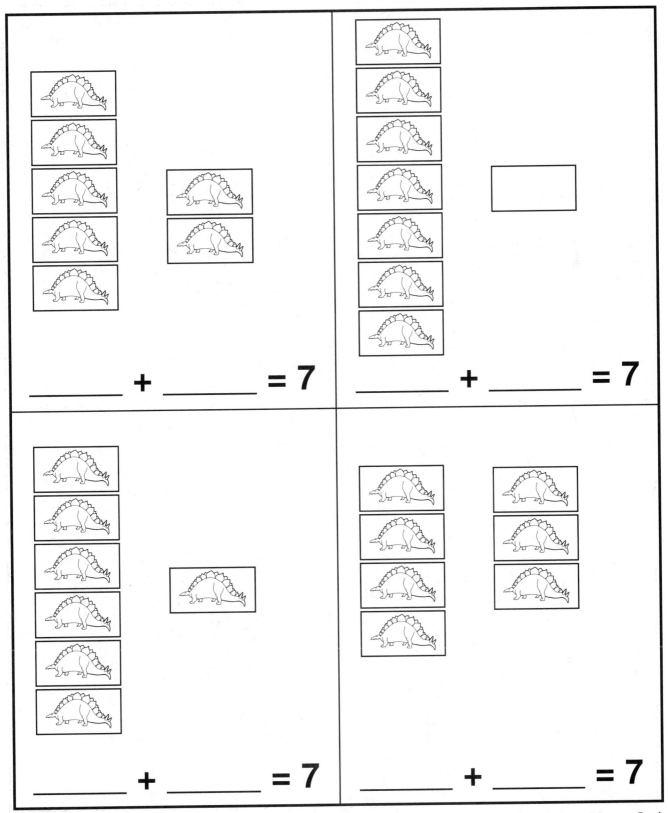

Number Combinations of 5, 6, 7, and 8

Teacher Directions: For each of the four sections, give students the correct number of manipulatives. Have each student divide the manipulatives into two groups to make different combinations of the number. Record the groups on the lines indicated. Sample: For the five section, give the student five blocks. The student divides the blocks into two groups, one group with three and the other with two. On the worksheet he or she records $3 + 2 = 5$. He or she then divides the blocks again to make two more different groups and records the results.

5		6

_____ + _____ = 5   _____ + _____ = 6

_____ + _____ = 5   _____ + _____ = 6

_____ + _____ = 5   _____ + _____ = 6

7		8

_____ + _____ = 7   _____ + _____ = 8

_____ + _____ = 7   _____ + _____ = 8

_____ + _____ = 7   _____ + _____ = 8

Picture Subtraction

Directions: Write a number sentence to show what is in each picture.
Example: There are seven palm trees, three are crossed off. The number sentence should read 7 – 3 = 4.

7 - _____ = _____   7 - _____ = _____

7 - _____ = _____   7 - _____ = _____

Addition and Subtraction Concepts

Teacher Directions: Show the students four bears, two in each of your hands. Close your hand over two of the bears. Ask the student "I have two bears in my hand, how many more do I need to make four?" Mark the student's response under the addition concept. Show the student four bears, two in each of your hands. Close your hand over two of the bears. Ask the student "If I take two bears away, how many bears do I have left?" Mark the student's response under the subtraction concept.

Concept of addition   yes   no

Concept of subtraction   yes   no

Connecting level: have the student read each picture sentence to you.

Connecting addition ——   yes   no

Connecting subtraction ——   yes   no

Symbolic level: Have the student write the number sentence for the pictures.

Addition

Subtraction

Problem solving: Read the problem and have the student solve the problem. The student may use manipulatives.

A. Three bears went swimming in a pond. Two bears got sleepy and went home. How many bears were left?

B. Five bears went to the lake to fish. Four more bears joined them. How many bears were at the lake?

       54

Gumdrop Drop

Directions: Drop a gumdrop onto the circle below ten times. Each time, record on the graph below whether it landed on the space marked X or O.

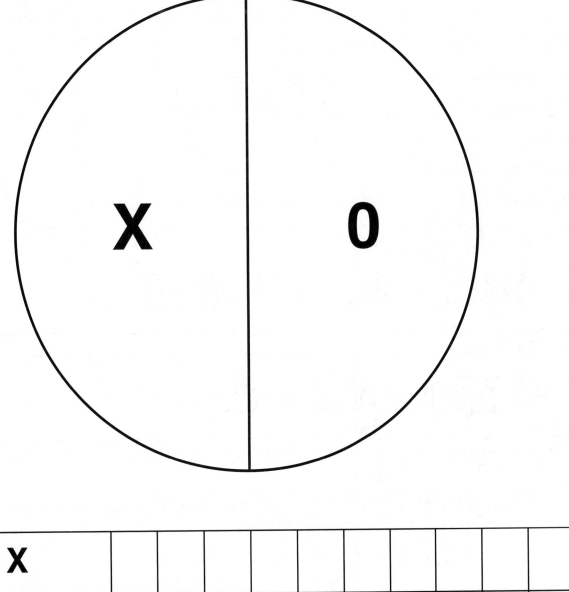

How many times did it land in each space? X _____ O _____

Estimation Graph

Teacher Directions: Fill three brown lunch bags with several objects that are the same. Use blocks, bears and crayons. Have the student guess how many he/she thinks are in each bag and write the number in the "estimation" square. The student may feel the bag, but not look inside. Then, have the student take out the objects, count them, and record the correct number in the "actual count" square. A discussion of the results should follow. Discuss with the student which bag had the most or least items, and whether their estimations were equal, higher, or lower than the actual amount.

	Estimation	Actual Count

Handfuls Graph

Teacher Directions: Fill four brown lunch bags with several blocks of one color. Put red in one bag, and do the same with green, yellow, and blue. Have the student write in the "Guess" box his or her guess of how many blocks will be pulled out in one handful. The student should then reach inside of the bag and remove one handful of blocks. Color the block on the graph. Have the student record the correct number of blocks in his or her hand in the "Count" box on the graph. Discuss what it means to estimate and how close the estimation was to the actual count.

Handfuls of Blocks

	Guess	Count
Red		
Green		
Yellow		
Blue		

Feed the Bear

Directions: Follow the directions for dividing each pie below for the hungry bear.

1. Feed the hungry bear a whole pie.

2. Feed the hungry bear half of the pie.

3. Feed the hungry bear one third of the pie.

4. Feed the hungry bear one fourth of the pie.

Fair Share for Bears

1. One bear eats 1 pie. Color the bear's share using only one color.

2. Each of the 2 bears gets ½ of the pie. Color each bear's share a different color.

3. Each of the 3 bears gets ⅓ of the pie. Color each bear's share a different color.

4. Each of the 4 bears gets ¼ of the pie. Color each bear's share a different color.

I Can Tell Time

Directions: On the line underneath each clock, write the time that is shown on the clock face. For problems 3 and 6, draw the hands on the clock face to represent the time shown underneath.

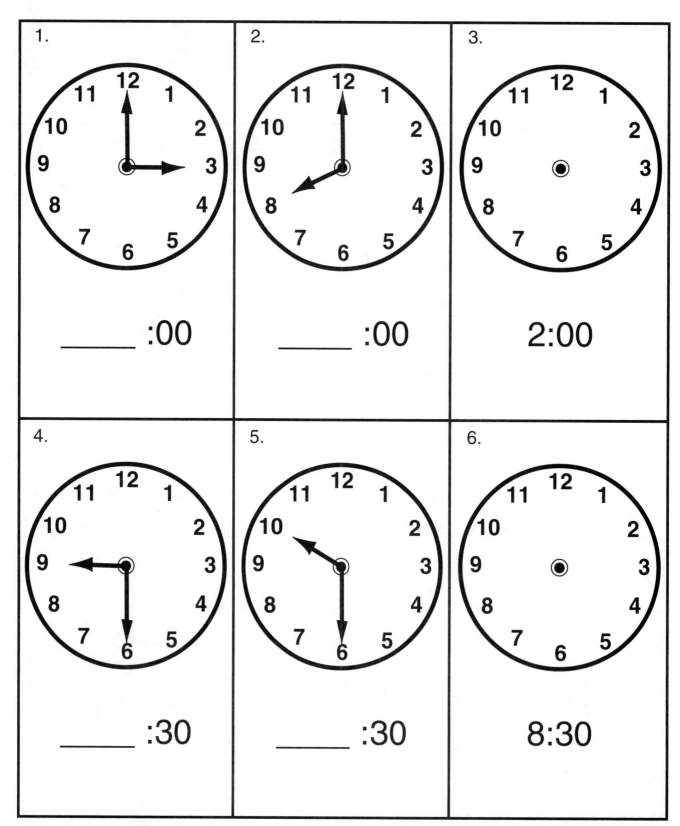

1. _____ :00

2. _____ :00

3. 2:00

4. _____ :30

5. _____ :30

6. 8:30

Digital Time

Directions: Circle the correct time that is being represented on the face of each digital clock.

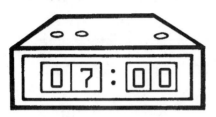

1.   7:00   4:00

2.   3:30   4:30

3.   11:30   12:30

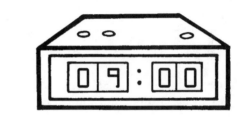

4.   9:00   6:00

5.   3:00   12:00

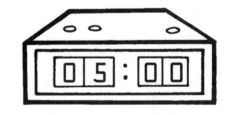

6.   5:00   5:30

7.   6:00   6:30

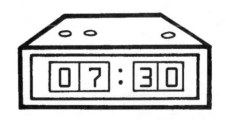

8.   7:00   7:30

Recognition of Coins

Teacher Directions: Show the student each coin and have them state the name of the coin and its value. Record the results below. It is recommended doing this three times during the year.

date	penny	nickel	dime	quarter
_____	_____	_____	_____	_____
_____	_____	_____	_____	_____
_____	_____	_____	_____	_____

date	value	value	value	value
_____	_____	_____	_____	_____
_____	_____	_____	_____	_____
_____	_____	_____	_____	_____

Teacher Directions: Give the student seven pennies, three nickels, two dimes, and two quarters. Ask the student to show you the amount asked for. Record the results below.

	one cent	two cents	five cents	ten cents	twenty-five cents
Date					
Date					
Date					

Notes: _____

_____

Money Combinations

Teacher Directions: Give the student enough coins to "buy" the items below. Have the student read the price tag and show the correct amount of coins needed to buy each item.

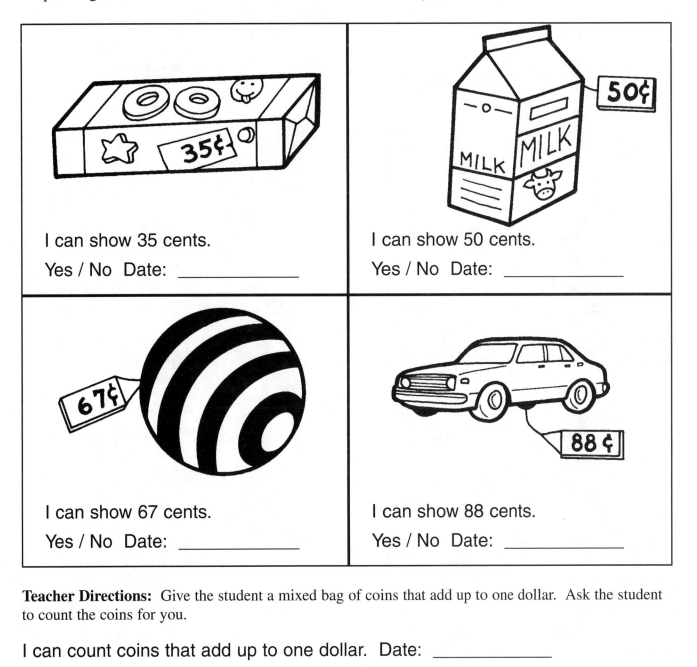

I can show 35 cents.

Yes / No Date: _____

I can show 50 cents.

Yes / No Date: _____

I can show 67 cents.

Yes / No Date: _____

I can show 88 cents.

Yes / No Date: _____

Teacher Directions: Give the student a mixed bag of coins that add up to one dollar. Ask the student to count the coins for you.

I can count coins that add up to one dollar. Date: _____

Notes: _____

_____

_____

_____

Piggy Banks

Teacher Directions: Give the student mixed coins in a bag. Ask the student to count out the correct amount of change for each piggy bank.

Time for School

Teacher Directions: Students may dictate the completion of the sentences with the teacher writing in the responses. Older students may fill in the blanks on their own using approximated spelling or conventional spelling.

My name is _____.

I am _____ years old.

My favorite thing I did this summer was _____.

Here is a picture I've drawn of myself:

Now I'm in School

My teacher's name is _____.

My friend's name is _____.

This year I will learn how to _____

_____.

The Name Page

Teacher Directions: Students will print their name in the space provided at different times during the school year. This page provides for handwriting comparisons throughout the year.

This is how I printed my name at the beginning of the school year.

Date: _____

This is how I printed my name at the middle of the school year.

Date: _____

This is how my name looks now.

Date: _____

I can print my first name. Yes No

I can print my last name. Yes No

Fall Inventory

Teacher Directions: Students may dictate the completion of the sentence stems with the teacher writing the responses. Older students may fill in the blanks on their own using approximated spelling or conventional spelling.

My favorite part of school is _____

_____.

The easiest thing for me to do at school is _____

_____.

The hardest thing for me to do at school is _____

_____.

Some of the new friends I've made at school are _____

and _____.

Here is a picture of me at school.

My Costume

Teacher Directions: It would be appropriate to fill out this page after a discussion about Halloween. Encourage the students to think about details when drawing themselves in their costume.

This year, I am dressing up as a

_____

_____.

I chose this costume because

_____

_____.

This is a picture I've drawn of myself in my costume.

Autumn

Teacher Directions: Use this page as a picture and story starter after a class discussion about fall.

In autumn I see _____

_____

_____

_____

_____

_____

_____

The Christmas Gift

Teacher Directions: Students may dictate the completion of the sentence stems with the teacher writing the responses on the lines provided. Older students may write their own responses using approximated spelling or conventional spelling. Have students draw a picture of the gift.

I would like to give my _____

a _____

_____

for Christmas.

I Wish

Teacher Directions: Students may dictate the completion of the sentence stem with the teacher writing the responses on the lines provided. Older students may write their own responses using approximated spelling or conventional spelling. At the bottom of the page let children try to draw the 100 items.

I wish I had one hundred _____

_____

_____.

One Hundred Day Celebration

Teacher Directions: Students may dictate the completion of the sentence stems with the teacher writing the responses in the lines provided. Older students may write their own responses using approximated spelling or conventional spelling.

If I had 100 _____,

I would _____

_____.

On the 100th Day of School, I celebrated

by _____

_____

_____

_____

_____.

My Dream

Teacher Directions: This is a picture and story starter for students to express their dream for humankind. This activity should be used after a discussion on the life of Dr. Martin Luther King, Jr.

My dream for all people is _____

_____

_____

_____

_____.

Winter Fun

Teacher Directions: This page is to be used as a picture and story starter after a class discussion about winter activities.

In the winter I like to… _____

_____

_____.

Groundhog Day

Teacher Directions: Reproduce this chart for each student. Give students five to seven minutes to walk around the room and ask their friends if they think the groundhog will see his shadow. The students have their friends sign their names in the yes or no column. After ten minutes, get together as a class and discuss the results. Discuss why the groundhog might or might not see his shadow. Use the page titled The Shadow (page 76) as a follow-up activity.

Will the groundhog see his shadow?

Yes	No

The Shadow

Teacher Directions: Use this page as a writing activity after a discussion on Groundhog Day. This would make a nice follow up to the page titled Groundhog Day.

The groundhog _____ see his shadow

because _____

_____

Do you think the groundhog really decides the weather?
Why or why not?

_____

_____

_____

_____

From My Heart

Teacher Directions: Students may dictate the completion of the sentence stems with the teacher writing the responses on the lines provided. Older students may write their own responses using approximated spelling or conventional spelling.

I would like to give a Valentine to _____

because _____

_____

_____.

Here's a picture of my special Valentine:

President's Day

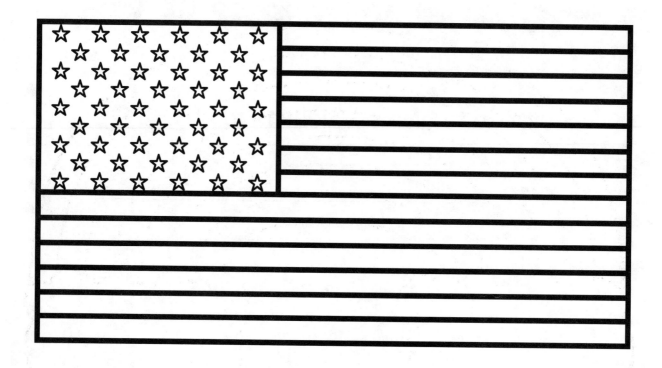

How many stars are on the American Flag? _____

How many stripes are on the American Flag?_____

Our first president was: _____

_____

Our current president is: _____

_____

The Rainbow

Teacher Directions: This page is to be used for a story starter after a discussion on rainbows or Saint Patrick's Day.

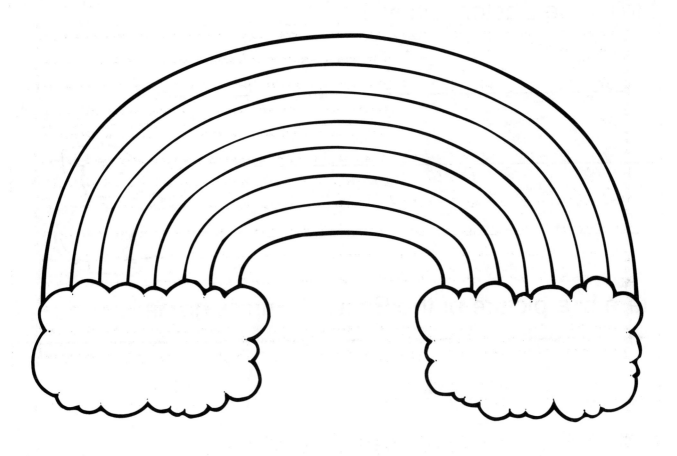

At the end of the rainbow, I would wish for _____

_____

_____

_____.

The Easter Bunny

Teacher Directions: This page is to be used as a story starter during the Easter season.

I think the Easter Bunny lives_____

_____

_____

_____ .

Here is a picture of the Easter Bunny's home.

Snack Time

Teacher Directions: Students may dictate the completion of the sentence stems with the teacher writing the responses on the lines provided. Older students may write their own responses using approximated spelling or conventional spelling.

I like to eat _____

for a snack.

I don't like to eat _____

for a snack.

I have _____

to drink at snack time.

I like to sit with _____

when I eat my snack.

Someday I hope we have _____

for a snack.

I hope we never have _____

at snack time.

Lunch

Teacher Directions: Students may dictate the completion of the sentence stems with the teacher writing in the responses in the lines provided. Older students may write their own responses using approximated spelling or conventional spelling.

I like to eat _____ for lunch.

I drink _____ with my lunch.

I like to sit with _____ .

I don't like _____ for lunch.

Recess

Teacher Directions: Students may dictate the completion of the sentence stems with the teacher writing the responses in the lines provided. Older students may write their own responses using approximated spelling or conventional spelling.

I like to play _____ at recess.

I play with _____ at recess.

The best thing about recess is _____

_____ .

Happy Birthday!

Teacher Directions: Students may dictate the completion of the sentence stems with the teacher writing the responses in the lines provided. Older students may write their own responses using approximated spelling or conventional spelling. Have the students draw candles on the cake to represent how old they are.

I am _____ years old.

My birthday is _____.

I would like a _____

for my birthday. Here is a picture of it.

My Address

Teacher Directions: Students may dictate the completion of the sentence stems with the teacher writing the responses in the lines provided. Older students may write their own responses using approximated spelling or conventional spelling.

I know my street address: _____

Date: _____

_____ Yes!   _____ I'm working on it.

I know my city: _____

Date: _____

_____ Yes!   _____ I'm working on it.

I know my state: _____

Date: _____

_____ Yes!   _____ I'm working on it.

Here is a picture of my house.

Friendly Letter

Teacher Directions: Discuss with your students why we write letters and how they were one of the first forms of long distance communication. Talk about the three main parts of the letter, the introduction, the body, and the closing. Ask your students to use the form below to write a friendly letter.

_____

(date)

_____

(greeting)

_____

_____

_____

(body)

_____

_____

_____

_____

(closing)

_____

(signature)

Envelope

Teacher Directions: Discuss with your students the proper way to address an envelope. Have them practice with the form below.

My Telephone

Teacher Directions: Students may dictate the completion of the sentence stems with the teacher writing the responses on the lines provided. Older students may write their own responses using approximated spelling or conventional spelling.

I can write my phone number:

_____ _____ _____ - _____ _____ _____ - _____ _____ _____ _____

I would like to call_____.

We would talk about _____.

We would talk for _____ minutes.

Watch Me Grow!

Teacher Directions: Weigh and measure the students, recording the results on the lines indicated.

Kindergarten Year

September   Weight _____   Height _____

January   Weight _____   Height _____

June   Weight _____   Height _____

First Grade Year

September   Weight _____   Height _____

January   Weight _____   Height _____

June   Weight _____   Height _____

My Teeth

Teacher Directions: Students may dictate the completion of the sentence stems with the teacher writing the responses on the lines provided. Older students may write their own responses using approximated spelling or conventional spelling. Have students draw in teeth.

I think I have _____ teeth.

I have lost _____ teeth.

I have _____ permanent teeth.

_____

makes me smile.

I feel _____

when I smile.

The Age of Dinosaurs

Teacher Directions: This page is to be used as a story starter after studying dinosaurs. It would also work well as a follow-up activity after reading a story about dinosaur facts.

If I had lived during the age of dinosaurs, I would have

_____

_____

_____

_____

Favorite Dinosaurs

Teacher Directions: This page is to be used as a story starter after studying dinosaurs. It would also work well as a follow-up activity after reading a story about dinosaur facts.

My favorite dinosaur is the _____.

I like it because _____

_____

_____

_____.

Senses Through the Seasons

Teacher Directions: After a unit on the five senses, help students fill in the blanks.
Example: In the fall, I see red leaves. Try to get the students to use all four seasons as well as the five senses.

1. In the _____

   I see_____.

2. In the _____

   I hear_____.

3. In the _____

   I smell _____.

4. In the _____

   I taste_____.

5. In the _____

   I feel_____.

I Like to Cook

Utensils

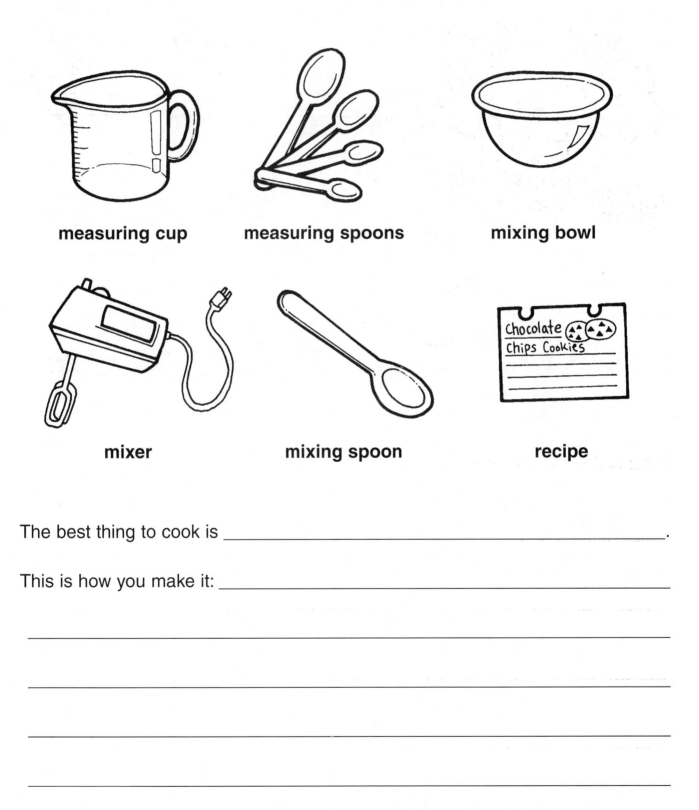

measuring cup   measuring spoons   mixing bowl

mixer   mixing spoon   recipe

The best thing to cook is _____.

This is how you make it: _____

_____

_____

_____

Spring

Teacher Directions: This picture and story starter should be used after a discussion on plants. Ask the students to add to the picture.

In the spring I like to grow_____

_____

_____

_____

_____.

Field Trip

Teacher Directions: This picture and story starter should be used as a follow-up to a class field trip.

Today we went on a class field trip to _____.

The two things that I liked best were:

1. _____

_____

_____

2. _____

_____

_____

Spring Inventory

Teacher Directions: Students may dictate the completion of the sentence stems with the teacher writing the responses in the lines provided. Older students may write their own responses using approximated spelling or conventional spelling.

I can write my name:

_____

What I liked the most about school this year was _____

_____.

The easiest thing for me to do at school this year was _____

_____.

The hardest thing for me to do at school this year was _____

_____.

Some of the new friends I've made this school year are _____

_____

_____

_____.

Story Map

Teacher Directions: Students may dictate the information needed to complete this story map with the teacher writing on the lines provided. Older students may complete this story map on their own.

Title of the book _____

Main character(s) _____

_____

_____

Setting _____

_____

_____

Problem _____

_____

_____

Solution _____

_____

_____

Story Sequence

Book Title: _____

Draw a picture or write a sentence to describe the three different parts of the story.

Beginning

_____

_____

_____

Middle

_____

_____

_____

End

_____

_____

_____

I Can Read All By Myself!

Teacher Directions: Use this page to record books that the student is able to read.

Title   **Date**

_____   _____

_____   _____

_____   _____

_____   _____

_____   _____

_____   _____

_____   _____

My Favorite Book

Teacher Directions: Students may dictate the completion of the sentence stems with the teacher writing the responses in the lines provided. Older students may write their own responses using approximated spelling or conventional spelling. This activity works well as an activity for children to do with their parents at home.

The name of my favorite book is _____

_____.

The author of the book is _____

_____.

This is what happened at the beginning of the book:

_____

_____

In the middle of the book:

_____

_____.

At the end of the book:

_____

_____

I liked this book because _____

_____

_____

Summer Fun

Teacher Directions: This page is to be used as a picture and story starter.

My favorite part of summer is _____

_____

_____

_____

_____ .

Autographs

Teacher Directions: Each student in the classroom writes his or her name on the sheet so that the students have autographs of all their classmates.

Memories

Teacher Directions: This page is for the students to draw pictures or display class photos of special events during the year.

☆ Field Trips ☆☆☆ Classroom Parties ☆☆☆ Special Events ☆

☆ Field Trips ☆☆☆ Classroom Parties ☆☆☆ Special Events ☆

Artist in Residence

Teacher Directions: This page is for the student to draw and display artwork. Because of limited space, you may want to make several copies of this page for each student, or take photographs of the artwork and glue the photos to the page.

Party Time

Teacher Directions: This picture and story starter should be used for the student to tell about his favorite school party.

The _____ party was my favorite

party because _____

_____

_____.

I Know These Colors!

Teacher Directions: Show the student color flashcards or crayons. Have the student identify each color and record the results below by circling the happy face or sad face. On the bottom half, use flashcards with the color words on them. Record the results as indicated.

Date: _____

red

blue

black

orange

brown

purple

pink

green

yellow

white

I know these color words:

_____ yellow

_____ red

_____ pink

_____ green

_____ white

_____ black

_____ blue

_____ orange

_____ purple

_____ brown

Rhyming Pictures

Draw a line between the two pictures that rhyme and have the same ending sound.

top

hen

pen

boat

goat

mop

Opposites

Teacher Directions: Show the student each row of pictures. Ask the student to identify the picture that is the opposite of the lead picture in each row. Have the student use a crayon to point to and circle the opposite picture.

Directions: Circle the opposite in each row.

happy	smiling	sad
up	down	right
little	medium	big
short	medium	tall

Real and Make-believe

(Fiction and Nonfiction)

Teacher Directions: Discuss with students the difference between real and make-believe, or fiction and nonfiction. Have each student write fiction or non-fiction under each picture and then color the pictures.

Cause and Effect

Teacher Directions: Discuss with the students how important it is to "read" pictures giving us important information when reading a book. Then, have students look at the first picture in each row. Ask them to circle the picture in the same row that shows what happened next. Remind them to pay attention to detail.

Positions
Heart Book

Teacher Directions: Cut apart and put together the Heart Book. Then follow the directions below each heart.

1. Put a sticker beside the heart.

2. Put a sticker over the heart.

3. Put a sticker under the heart.

4. Put a sticker on top of the heart.

Classifying

Directions: Circle the object that does not belong in the group.

carrots	book	beans	potatoes

canoe	boat	ship	apple

Mitten Match

Directions: Cut out the mittens and paste them on the correct snowman. Then, color the picture.

Fire Safety
Stop, Drop, and Roll

Directions: Put the stop, drop, and roll pictures in the correct order. Write the number under the picture.

_____   _____   _____

Directions: Draw a picture or write words to describe your home escape route.

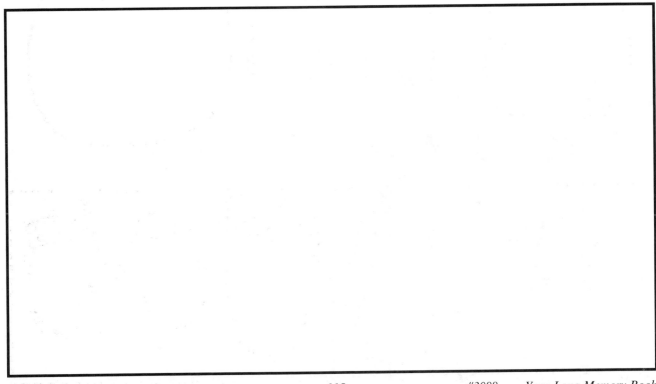

Gift Sequence

Directions: Write 1, 2, 3, or 4 on the line in each square to show the order in which the girl wraps the gift.

Picture Sequence

Directions: Put the pictures in the correct order by writing 1, 2, or 3 on the line provided.

Tornado Safety

Directions: Put the pictures that describe what to do in case of a tornado in order by writing 1, 2, or 3 on the lines provided.

When there is a tornado I find a safe place.

_____

When there is a tornado I face the wall, kneel, and cover my head.

_____

When there is a tornado I wait patiently until an adult tells me it's safe to move around again.

_____

Teacher Directions: Have the child describe where is his or her house he or she would go in case of a tornado. Then, have them draw a picture of it.

I know a safe place in my home.

From Tree to Market

Directions: Color and cut apart the pictures. Paste them in order in the frame below.

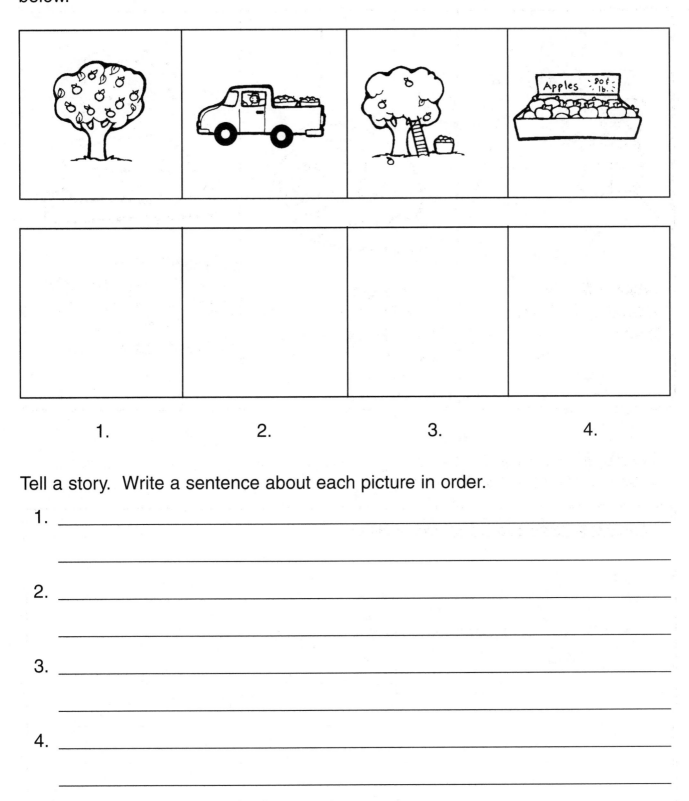

1.   2.   3.   4.

Tell a story. Write a sentence about each picture in order.

1. _____

_____

2. _____

_____

3. _____

_____

4. _____

_____

Seasons of a Tree

Match the picture to the season. Write the sentences in order on the lines below.

3.

The apples are ready to be picked.

Spring

4.

The tree can rest—no more apples.

Summer

2.

The apples grow bigger every day.

Fall

1.

The apple blossoms begin to grow.

Winter

1. _____

2. _____

3. _____

4. _____

Life Cycles

Directions: Number the following pictures to show the correct order of the life cycle of a frog and a butterfly. Place the number in the box.

The Life Cycle of a Frog

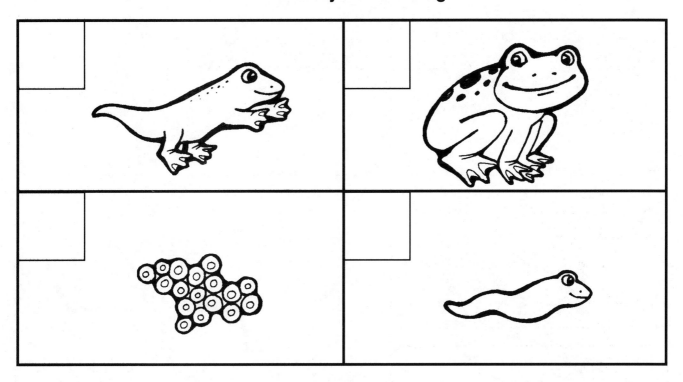

The Life Cycle of a Butterfly

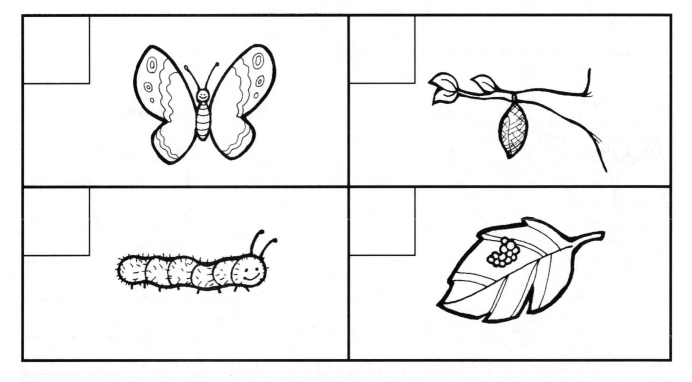

Butterfly Life Cycle

Directions:

Color the pictures below. Then cut out each picture and glue on a separate piece of paper, in order, to show the life cycle of a butterfly. Number each section of the life cycle.

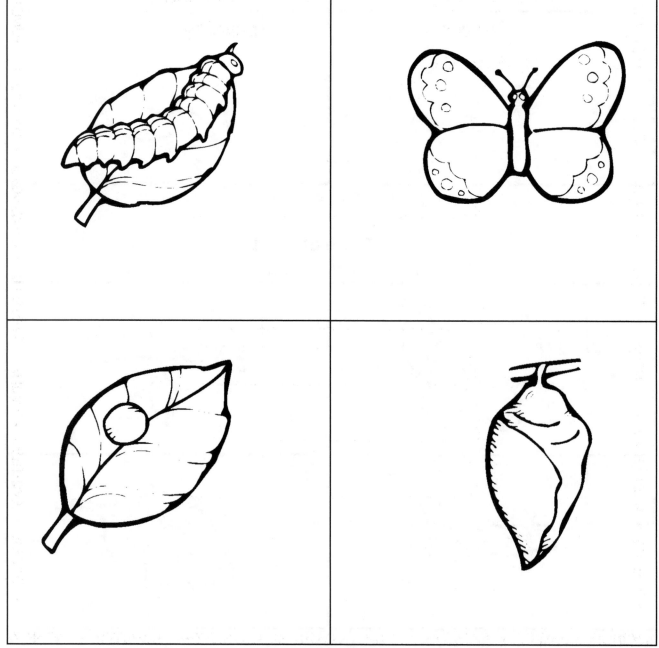

Sequencing
Days of the Week

Directions: The days of the week are all mixed up. Recopy the days of the week in the correct order, on the lines below.

• THURSDAY • FRIDAY • SATURDAY • SUNDAY • MONDAY • TUESDAY • WEDNESDAY SATURDAY •

Friday   **Thursday**

Tuesday   **Wednesday**

Sunday   **Monday**

Saturday

1. _____

2. _____

3. _____

4. _____

5. _____

6. _____

7. _____

Days of the Week/Months of the Year

Teacher Directions: Students may dictate the completion of the sentence stems with the teacher writing the responses in the lines provided. Older students may write their own responses using approximated spelling or conventional spelling.

Days of the Week

I can say the days of the week.

Date: _____

_____ I can do it by myself.

_____ I'm working on it.

I like _____ the best because
_____day of the week_____

_____.

Months of the Year

I can say the months of the year.

Date: _____

_____ I can do it by myself.

_____ I'm working on it.

My favorite month is _____.

I like it because_____

_____.

Matching Letters

Directions: Find the letters in each line that are the same as the letter in the box and put an "X" on them.

R	R	B	P	R	R
F	H	E	F	F	F
N	H	N	M	K	N
W	V	W	M	W	M
G	Q	G	O	C	G
P	R	S	P	P	P
C	O	D	G	C	C
Q	O	Q	D	Q	C

Matching Upper and Lower Case Letters

Directions: Draw a line to match the upper case letter to the correct lower case letter in each box.

A	f
B	a
C	c
D	b
E	e
F	d

N	s
O	r
P	q
Q	p
R	o
S	n

G	i
H	g
I	h
J	k
K	j
L	l
M	m

T	z
U	w
V	y
W	t
X	u
Y	x
Z	v

Lower Case Letters

Directions: Trace over the shaded guide to form the lower case letters.

Aa Bb Cc

Aa	Bb	Cc
Dd	Ee	Ff
Gg	Hh	Ii
Jj	Kk	Ll

Lower Case Letters *(cont.)*

Directions: Trace over the shaded guide to form the lower case letters.

	Mm	Nn
Oo	Pp	Qq
Rr	Ss	Tt
Uu	Vv	Ww
Xx	Yy	Zz

Letter Printing

Teacher Directions: Students should copy the model of each letter provided by writing their own letter on the spaces provided. This page may be copied several times for each student to make comparisons throughout the school year.

A _____ a _____   I _____ i _____

B _____ b _____   J _____ j _____

C _____ c _____   K _____ k _____

D _____ d _____   L _____ l _____

E _____ e _____   M _____ m _____

F _____ f _____   N _____ n _____

G _____ g _____   O _____ o _____

H _____ h _____   P _____ p _____

Letter Printing *(cont.)*

Teacher Directions: Students should copy the model of each letter provided by writing their own letter on the spaces provided. This page may be copied several times for each student to make comparisons throughout the school year.

Q _____ q _____   Y _____ y _____

R _____ r _____   Z _____ z _____

S _____ s _____

T _____ t _____

U _____ u _____

V _____ v _____

W _____ w _____

X _____ x _____

Letter Identification

Teacher Directions: Have the student identify the letters below. Mark off the letters the student can identify. Record the results at the bottom of the page.

I can identify these letters:

M	S	N	G	H	D	J
B	T	L	K	A	F	
E	P	I	Z	X	R	
O	V	W	Y	U	C	Q

m	s	n	g	h	d	j
b	t	l	k	a	f	
e	p	i	z	x	r	
o	v	w	y	u	c	q

Upper Case

Date:_____ ___ /26   Date:_____ ___ /26

Date:_____ ___ /26   Date:_____ ___ /26

Lower Case

Date:_____ ___ /26   Date:_____ ___ /26

Date:_____ ___ /26   Date:_____ ___ /26

Picture and Sound Match

Directions: Match the picture with its beginning letter sound.

M m

S s

G g

Q q

D d

B b

T t

L l

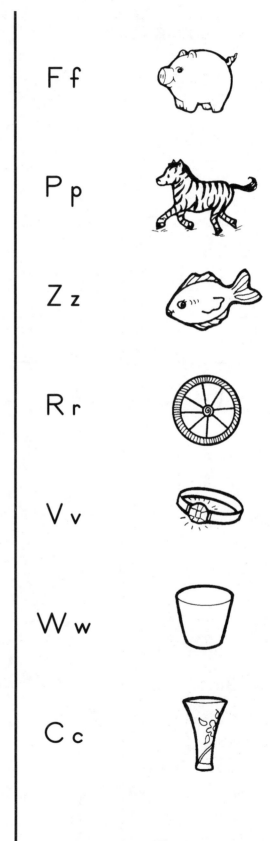

F f

P p

Z z

R r

V v

W w

C c

Initial Consonant Sounds

Directions: Circle the letter that shows the beginning sound of the picture in the box.

b t	c d	t b
h l	f b	h m
c t	m c	f t
d t	h d	h b

Letter/Sound Relationships

Directions: Print the letter that represents the beginning sound for each picture.

Sight Words

Directions: Write the name of each picture on the lines provided.

Fill in the Missing Letters

Directions: Write in the missing letters to complete the name of each picture.

c _ _

n _ _

d _ _

h _ _

b _ _

s _ _

b _ _

c _ _

p _ _

t _ _

b _ _

p _ _

ABC Fill In

Directions: Write in the missing letters for the upper and lower case alphabet.

A	B			E
	G		I	K
M		O		Q	S
T			W		Z

	a	b			e
f		h		k
	n		p		s
t		v		x	

Rhyming Words

Directions: Write the missing rhyming word that completes the sentence on the line provided.

The bug is on a _____.

The cat has a _____.

The frog is on the _____.

The hen is in the _____.

The cake is on the _____.

Phonemic Awareness Practice

Teacher Directions: Phonemic Awareness has become a very big part of the primary classroom. Use the activities below as a way to help your students understand this concept. These are whole group activities that can be used when sitting on the rug, while waiting in line, or as a lesson in class. Explain to the students that words are made of letters and each of the letters in a word is responsible for making a sound. When combined, the sounds make up the word that we hear. Say a word in segments and have the students guess what the word is that you are saying.

Examples:

s-o-m-e	some
f-un	fun
c-ow	cow
s-p-a-c-e	space

Note: Demonstrate how words break up by writing them on a chalkboard or white board. *Only do this as a demonstration, as phonemic awareness is all oral.*

Teacher Directions: Now, ask students to identify if a specific sound is heard at the beginning or end of a word. Say the sound that you're looking for first and then say the word.

Examples:

/t/	flat
/p/	soup
/k/	kite
/h/	help
/l/	light
/n/	can

Note: This as a whole group lesson first and then use these simple and short activities to fill extra minutes throughout the day. The more practice the students get, the better. Remember, phonemic awareness is all oral; don't ask your students to separate the words on paper.

Look At All the Words I Can Write!

Teacher Directions: Ask the student to record words he/she can spell correctly. Do this activity twice during the school year, or have the student add words as he/she learns them. This page may be reproduced several times for each student.

Beginning Sight Words

Name: _____ Date: _____

Teacher Directions: Ask the student to read each sight word out loud. You may put the words on flashcards if you prefer. Do this two to three times during the year.

Date _____ % _____		Date _____ % _____	
I	go	is	to
in	see	it	and
me	my	the	up

Date _____ % _____		Date _____ % _____	
no	can	a	dad
at	you	look	red
he	she	mom	blue

Level One
Sight Words

Name: _____ Date: _____

Teacher Directions: Have the student read each sight word to you. You may put the words on flashcards if you prefer. Do this two to three times during the year.

Date _____ % _____		Date _____ % _____		Date _____ % _____	
a	are	he	she	boy	book
as	animal	him	to	ball	from
at	and	her	too	by	friend
an	about	has	they	be	gone
am		have	take	baby	give
		here	them		
		see			

Date _____ % _____		Date _____ % _____		Date _____ % _____	
I	the	can	did	look	up
in	very	could	girl	me	will
it	would	can't	go	my	you
is	won't	come	get	no	year
not	went	do	got	on	zoo
never	put			off	jump
name				of	

Emergent Literacy Skill Assessment

Name: _____ Date: _____

Teacher Directions: This page may be reproduced several times for each student. It is recommended that you use this assessment at least twice during the school year.

Reading Readiness Skill Assessment

Identifies upper case letters _____ /26

Identifies lower case letters _____ /26

Demonstrates knowledge of letter/sound
correspondence (consonants) _____ /20

Identifies sight words presented _____ /68

Demonstrates knowledge of the following concepts about print:

	Yes	No
Holds book correctly	_____	_____
Identifies front/back of book	_____	_____
Identifies top/bottom of page	_____	_____
Identifies beginning/middle/end book	_____	_____
Indicates print contains message	_____	_____
Utilizes picture clues to predict text	_____	_____
Follows predictable text patterns	_____	_____
Differentiates between letter/word	_____	_____
Identifies position: first/last letter in a word	_____	_____
Utilizes some initial consonants to predict words	_____	_____
Utilizes meaning cues to predict words	_____	_____

When tracking print, demonstrates the following:

	Yes	No
Left to right directionality	_____	_____
Return sweep	_____	_____
Top to bottom directionality	_____	_____
One-to-one correspondence	_____	_____

Beginning Writing Skill Assessment

	Yes	No
Copies words and phrases	_____	_____
Uses developmental spelling:		
Prints random letters	_____	_____
Prints first letter in a word	_____	_____
Prints final letter in a word	_____	_____
Prints some complete words	_____	_____

Phonemic Awareness Assessment

Name: _____ Date: _____

Teacher Directions: This assessment should be given to each student individually. Read each word to the student separating each sound in the word. Then, ask the student to identify the word.

Blending

Words in segments

s-un	sun	_____		c-an	can	_____
c-up	cup	_____		t-op	top	_____
h-en	hen	_____		sh-i-p	ship	_____

Blended beginning

p-l-a-te	plate	_____		b-l-ue	blue	_____
f-l-i-p	flip	_____		s-t-o-p	stop	_____
s-p-i-n	spin	_____		b-r-ea-k	break	_____

Blended ending

k-i-n-d	kind	_____		s-i-n-k	sink	_____
r-a-m-p	ramp	_____		ch-i-l-d	child	_____
f-a-s-t	fast	_____		r-i-n-g	ring	_____

Phoneme Isolation

Directions: Have the student identify if the specific sound is at the beginning or ending of the said word.

hide	/h/	_____		plate	/p/	_____
pot	/t/	_____		head	/d/	_____
cheese	/ch/	_____		lip	/p/	_____
boot	/t/	_____		coat	/c/	_____
run	/r/	_____		dish	/sh/	_____